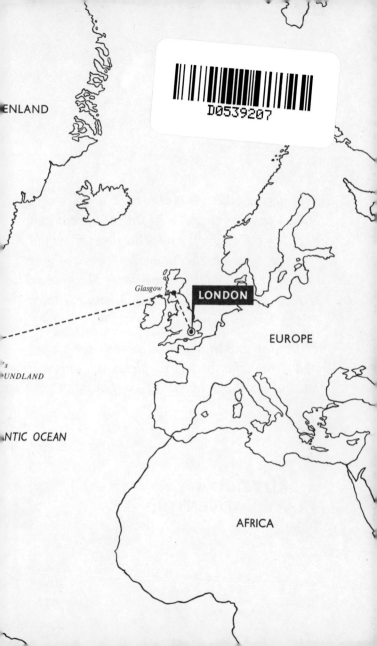

Series 587

Fly across the Atlantic to Canada with Alison and John and explore that great and exciting country. Travel with them from old Quebec through the boundless wheat-lands and over the mighty Rockies. Meet their friends, especially Trapper Joe with his tales of the Frozen North.

From the adventures of Alison and John, and from the beautiful pictures, you will learn a lot—and you will have fun!

**A LADYBIRD
TRAVEL ADVENTURE
BOOK**

FLIGHT TWO:
CANADA

by
DAVID SCOTT DANIELL

Illustrated by
JACK MATTHEW

Publishers: Wills & Hepworth Ltd., Loughborough

First Published 1959   © *Printed in England*

Alison and John sat in one of the front seats in the air-liner. Their father sat behind. They were wonderfully comfortable seats, which you could tilt back to make a kind of bed. That was a good thing, because they were going to fly through the night right across the Atlantic Ocean to Canada.

John looked at his birthday-present wrist watch. " It's a quarter-past eight," he said to Alison, " nearly my bedtime! And look, we're off ! "

They waved through the window towards the balcony of the Airport buildings, where they knew their Mother and young Peter and baby Mary would be waving to them. The great air-liner sped down the runway and then left the ground, folding up its landing wheels. As they climbed, London Airport grew smaller and smaller.

They flew north up the middle of England to Glasgow, and then swung west and set their course across the Atlantic. Below them the top of the clouds looked like a sea of fluffy cotton-wool, coloured pink by the setting sun. When there was a break in the clouds they saw the sea far, far below.

The friendly steward and stewardess brought them a delicious dinner of all the nicest things, arranged on trays with partitions. Afterwards they had a great thrill when the Captain himself invited them into the control cabin. John was quite speechless with wonder. When they went back to their seats they tilted them and settled down. Soon they were fast asleep, many thousand feet above the sea, flying at three hundred miles an hour towards Canada.

4

7214 0144 9

They landed at Montreal early the next morning. As they walked from the gangway towards the airport buildings Alison suddenly stopped and stood quite still, with her eyes closed. Her father looked surprised and asked if she had left something behind in the aeroplane. She shook her head.

" No," she said, " I'm just realising that I am truly standing in Canada! "

John stood still and shut his eyes as well.

" I know what you mean," said their father, "it *is* exciting. Yes, this is Canada. By the time we have finished our travels I hope you will both know something about this great country and the Canadian people. But come on now, to our hotel."

Their father had come to Canada to visit business friends, and he had brought Alison and John so that they could travel with him and also visit their cousins in Alberta.

On their first day their father did no business, but took them round the city of Montreal. As well as sight-seeing the children learned that in Canada the traffic drives on the right side of the road, and that instead of pounds, shillings and pence, they use Canadian dollars. They have a hundred cents to the dollar, which John thought very sensible and a help in doing sums.

They visited the beautiful park on Mount Royal and drove through busy streets with the modern buildings, but with a few old ones tucked away among them. They liked the port best of all, where enormous liners were moored in the St. Lawrence River, a thousand miles inland. They liked the bridges too, and the silver-coloured train setting out on its three thousand mile journey across Canada.

Alison and John spent a happy week in Montreal, sight-seeing and getting used to Canada. They met some of their father's business friends and went to their homes. The Canadian children asked them a lot of questions about England, and wanted to know all about the Queen, the Prince of Wales and Princess Anne, and all sorts of things. At the end of the week they had to pack their suit-cases for their first journey in Canada, five hundred miles eastwards to Nova Scotia.

In the aeroplane Alison asked, "Does Nova Scotia mean New Scotland?"

" It does. Well done," said her father.

" Is it a Scottish country, then ? " John asked.

" It's a bit like Scotland," his father said, "it's got a wild and rugged coast-line and lovely scenery. And they play the bagpipes, and a lot of people speak Gaelic. But it was French first of all, for they settled here in 1604."

That's over three hundred and fifty years ago," said Alison.

" It's the oldest part of Canada," her father said. " We fought over it for a hundred years until in 1713 it became British and it was called Nova Scotia."

Their father visited business friends in Halifax, the capital of Nova Scotia. It was another great port, where liners from Europe stop in the winter when the St. Lawrence is frozen. The children had lovely motor drives and saw mile after mile of apple orchards, farms, magnificent forests and coal mines. They all spent the week-end in a dreamy little fishing village and went out in a fishing boat. The fisherman gave them some of the best fish to take to the hotel. They had them for supper and they were the nicest fish they had ever eaten.

Their next journey took them further eastwards, to the province of Newfoundland, an island which is the nearest part of Canada to Europe. This time it was John who noticed something interesting about the name, as they were flying over the sea between Nova Scotia and Newfoundland.

" It's just come to me," he said suddenly, " the name must mean exactly what it says, —new-found-land! "

" It meant that once, John, my boy," said his father, " but that was a long time ago. John Cabot, the great explorer, sailed from Bristol in 1497 and discovered what was then 'new-found-land' indeed. He claimed it for the King of England."

" Nearly five hundred years ago! " said Alison.

" Yes. Soon afterwards fishermen from Devon came and they settled. Newfoundland was our oldest colony of all. It became a province of Canada in 1949."

" So Newfoundland is Canada's newest province," said John.

" I'd say it was the oldest," said Alison.

" For once you are both right," said their father, " it is the newest province and the oldest colony."

They stayed for a few days in St. John's, the capital of Newfoundland, exploring the city and travelling by car into the wild and lovely countryside. One day a friend took them on a salmon fishing trip in a beautiful river amidst dense forest. They had a picnic and watched their father and his friend catch some big, shining salmon. Once they heard a great noise on the opposite bank and saw a bull moose come through the trees and stand there proudly. He was a splendid animal and Alison and John kept very quiet as they watched him.

When their father had finished his business in New-foundland they flew westwards to Quebec. Quebec is on the St. Lawrence River a hundred and sixty miles east of Montreal. As they were sitting at a table outside a cafe, eating ice-creams, John said, " I didn't know people in Canada spoke French! "

" Everyone seems to speak French here," said Alison.

" There is a very good reason," their father said. "Four out of every five persons in Quebec are French-Canadians."

" But why? " John asked. " I thought Canada was British."

"And so are the French-Canadians," their father explained. "You see, Canada was French first of all. Then General Wolfe defeated the French General Montcalm in a big battle outside Quebec. That was in 1759, and soon afterwards Canada became British. The French people wanted to go on living here and it was agreed that they should keep their own language and customs. They still do, but they are true Canadians."

" What a very nice way to arrange it," said Alison.

" Because of the two languages," their father said, "all official speeches are made twice, in English and in French."

In the afternoon they explored old Quebec, with its ancient walls right round the city. They went to the Plains of Abraham where the battle was fought, and saw the narrow path up which the British soldiers climbed from their boats in the St. Lawrence below, and the very spot where General Wolfe died in battle. Then they wandered happily round the old citadel of Quebec, gazing from the ramparts and looking at the old cannons. They tried to imagine what it was like in 1759, when a battle won a whole great nation for Britain.

They stayed with one of their father's business friends in Quebec. Madame Le Brun took Alison and John for expeditions, and they made friends with young Jacques and Anne-Marie Le Brun. The Le Brun family spoke French among themselves, but they spoke perfect English as well. At the week-end they all went to the Le Bruns' country cottage, a log-built house in the Laurentian hills. There was a wonderful view, a sparkling stream and fine woods.

One afternoon, when Monsieur Le Brun and their father were fishing for rainbow trout, the four children went for a ramble and stood dead still to watch a beaver nibbling at a bit of wood.

" They're very clever," said Jacques. " You ought to see the dams they build in the river in the Autumn. They do it to make the water deep so that it won't freeze to the bottom of the river."

" And they build their homes, called lodges, in the dam," Anne-Marie added.

Marie showed them some maple trees and Jacques gave them each a leaf. " It's the emblem of Canada." he explained.

" You ought to see the maples in the Autumn," Anne-Marie said, " they turn a glorious red and gold colour, like fire."

Anne-Marie asked Alison if she had seen the Queen often. " We saw her when she came to Canada," she said proudly.

" It must have been a thrill," said Alison, "living here, to see the Queen of England."

Both the French-Canadian children spoke at once.

" In Canada, she is the Queen of Canada! " said Jacques.

" Not the Queen of *England* here," said Anne-Marie, " the Queen of Canada! "

When their visit to the Le Brun family in Quebec came to an end they went to Ottawa. They travelled by train nearly three hundred miles westwards, passing through Montreal again. It was easy to see that Ottawa, with its stately buildings and fine houses, was the capital of all Canada.

The first trip they made was to Parliament Hill, where they gazed at the tall Peace Tower.

"It's very like the tower of our own Parliament buildings," John said, unslinging his camera, "the one with Big Ben."

"The Canadian Parliament is like the British one, too," their father explained. "They have their own Prime Minister, Cabinet Ministers and Members of Parliament, and the Governor General represents the Queen. When the Queen was in Canada, Her Majesty opened Parliament, as she does in London."

Alison and John then asked their father about the famous Canadian Mounted Police. He explained that they were formed about eighty years ago to keep law and order in the wild, western parts. They were then called the Canadian North West Mounted Police, but are now called the Royal Canadian Mounted Police. Their main task is to patrol the distant parts of Canada.

He told them that until a few years ago the 'mountie' wore a colourful uniform and rode a horse when on duty. Now he wears his red and blue uniform only on very special ceremonial occasions. The 'mountie' is more likely to be seen in a brown and blue uniform and riding a large, fast motor-cycle.

After they had spent a few days in Ottawa they went on another train journey to Toronto, and from there they went to see the Niagara Falls. They gazed with awe at this wonder of the world. The clear water tumbled in a sparkling cascade into the swirling, foaming river. There was a continuous awe-inspiring roar of sound.

" It's no use," said Alison, closing her sketch book, " I just can't draw it! "

" The only thing to do," said her father, " is to look and listen, and marvel! "

John took out his notebook and pencil ready to write down the facts. " How high are they? " he asked.

" It's all in the guide-book here," his father replied. " Wait a minute. Ah, here we are. Ready? The Canadian Falls, the ones opposite us, are 162 feet high and 2,600 feet wide at the top. They are called the Horse-shoe Falls, and you can see why if you look at the crest."

John wrote quickly, not bothering much about the spelling, and then he looked up for more information.

" The other falls—over there, see—are the American Falls. They are five feet higher, but less than half as wide— about a thousand feet.

John wrote that down and Alison studied the map.

" I see the Niagara River links Lake Erie with Lake Ontario," she said.

" That's right," her father said, " and the Niagara River divides Canada from America." John wrote that down.

" I came here once in winter," he went on, "and it was an extraordinary sight. The Falls were frozen solid. The ice hung in twisted columns and stood up in tall crystal pinacles. The river below was solid, too, and looked just like whipped cream! "

" My goodness," said Alison, " and look at it now! "

" And listen to it," said John.

Their father had a lot of business in Toronto, near the Niagara Falls, and they stayed there a week. Toronto, the Capital of the Province of Ontario, is a busy, bustling city and Alison and John had a very interesting time. Their next journey was very exciting. They went by ship six hundred miles across Lake Huron and Lake Superior to Port Arthur.

As the brightly-painted steamer slipped through the blue water, their father spread the map of Canada on the deck and they looked at the great lakes.

" How big are they? " John asked.

" About three hundred miles long and up to a hundred and fifty miles wide in places. "

" They're more like seas than lakes," Alison said. " Everything in Canada is so *big*! "

Canada is the second largest country in the world. It's larger than the United States of America."

" Look," said John, " Canada goes right up to the Arctic."

"Someone once told me," said his father, " that if you could hinge Canada on the east coast, say at Halifax, and then turn it over, it would cover the Atlantic and half Europe as well! "

Alison ran a finger along the map. " The boundary between Canada and America from the Pacific coast goes almost in a straight line as far as Lake Superior."

" Then it goes along the middle of the lakes," said John, " up the St. Lawrence and then wriggles to the east coast. "

" The boundary is nearly four thousand miles long," said his father, " and because Canada and America are such good friends there are no frontier posts or frontier guards."

Alison, John and their father stood on the deck of the steamer looking forward to Port Arthur as their lovely voyage ended.

" So far," said their father, " you've only seen the old part of Canada. Now you are going to see something of the new Canada."

" What do you mean, old and new Canada? " John asked.

" Well, at first people settled only near the sea and down the St. Lawrence River. The rest of Canada was almost unknown, it was the home of Red Indians and wild animals. Only missionaries and fur trappers ventured there or travelled west. Then about seventy years ago they built the great Canadian Pacific Railway right across Canada, roads were made, and people moved west. Many of them settled in the Prairie provinces."

" Which are the Prairie provinces? " Alison asked.

" Manitoba, Saskatchewan and Alberta. They stretch across the middle of Canada, from Ontario, where we've just been, to the Rocky Mountains. It's the great wheat-growing country. Do you see that ship coming out of Port Arthur? She is loaded with wheat."

"What are all those very tall buildings on the docks there, with ships tied up alongside them? " John asked.

" They're grain elevators. The wheat is brought to Port Arthur, or to its nearby twin city, Fort William, in railway trucks. It is loaded into those elevators, graded according to the quality and inspected by Government officials. Then it is *poured* into the holds of the ships. The ships take it across the lakes to ports like Montreal, Quebec, or Halifax in Newfoundland. There it is loaded into ocean-going ships and is taken to Europe. Canada provides the flour for the bread of millions of people all over the world."

They went from Port Arthur by train to Winnipeg, the capital of Manitoba province. Their father told them that only eighty years ago Winnipeg was a tiny trading post right out in the wilds. Now it is a busy modern city, the principal market for the grain grown in the Canadian farm lands.

After a few days in Winnipeg they went by train three hundred miles into Saskatchewan to visit Uncle James and his family. He met them at the station and took them in his car nearly a hundred miles through glorious farmland to his own farm. There they met Auntie Ethel and their cousins Philip, Helen and Martin. They were all rather shy at first, meeting for the first time. Alison and John gave them presents they had brought from England. Their shyness didn't last long and soon they were all chattering happily.

The house was large and modern. It was built of wood, and the windows and doors were specially made, so that extra ones could be added to keep the house warm in the long, very cold winter. It was a great occasion to have their English cousins visiting them, and in the evening there was a party. The farm men came and a few neighbours from ten miles away or more. There was an enormous supper and then Square-dancing, to the music of a fiddle played by a grizzled old man called Trapper Joe. Alison and John were very tired and very happy when at last they went to bed.

The next morning Alison and John were taken round the farm buildings by their cousins. They saw the gigantic barns, and so many tractors and complicated farm machines that it was more like a factory than a farm. Alison noticed a huge pile of wood, sawn ready for the winter.

They explored the farm, admired the machinery, fed the ponies and cuddled the baby calves. Then they all went to see their cousins' grandmother, Auntie Ethel's mother. She was sitting in her rocking chair on the porch. The children sat round her on the floor, drinking milk and eating doughnuts.

" Was all this just prairie when you first came? " Alison asked after a while.

" Just untamed prairie, my dear," the old lady said. " The first thing we did was to build our house, only one room, and a stable for our two horses. We laid in a store of fuel for the winter, and enough flour and bacon and beans to see us through. My, that first winter! " She fell silent, thinking of the far-off days.

" Which land did you plough up first? " Helen asked.

" Why the land opposite us now. How we worked when spring came, from before daylight until dark! We were lucky, and in the fall we took our sacks of wheat to the railroad, and that was the beginning. As the years passed we built a proper house, and barns, bought more horses and had more and more hired hands living here for the summer. With God's blessing we prospered."

" How wonderful to have *made* all this! " said John, as he looked round at the ripening wheat which stretched as far as he could see.

" Things are easier now," said the old lady. " They have tractors and combine-harvesters, and quick transport to the grain elevators. Clever scientists test the soil and discover the best grain to use. But the real things are the same. Hard work in the open air. The miracle of the growing corn. The excitement of harvest time. And best of all, after the long winter, the wonder of the spring! "

26

The children had been playing rounders until they were so hot that they flopped down in the shade of some trees. "Oh, it's so hot," Alison said, " I just can't imagine it ever being cold here."

" It's cold all right in winter," said Philip.

" We have snow in England," said John, " but most years as soon as we get the sledge mended it's gone! "

" It doesn't go here in a hurry," said Helen. " In the fall—what you call the autumn—we get a few frosts and all the trees go golden, and then along comes the killing frost, and winter starts."

" Then it snows," said Martin, " thick and heavy, and it just stays, frozen solid, until the spring—five long months."

" And the spring," said Helen, " makes you want to dance and shout, it's so wonderful! "

" What clothes do you wear? " Alison asked.

" Thick and warm," said Philip.

" And fur caps," said Helen, " with flaps over our ears. Otherwise they'd get frost-bitten."

" And we wear double mittens," Martin said. "If we wore ordinary gloves in the winter our fingers would get frost-bitten. And we wear real Indian-made moccasins."

" They're long boots of soft leather," Philip explained· " Your toes would freeze if you wore ordinary boots."

" And you have to rub your nose often," said Helen, " or twitch it like a rabbit as Martin does, or that would be frost-bitten too."

" If you see someone's nose going white," Philip said, " you rub snow on it quickly."

" Yes it's cold all right out here in the winter," Martin said.

One of their best friends on the farm was old Joe the trapper, who had played the violin so well at the party. He worked at odd jobs on the farm every summer, but when the first snow fell he set off alone to the far northland, fur trapping.

" How do you do it, Joe? " John asked him as they sat talking by a pile of logs.

" How do I do it, sonny? " Joe repeated, looking at John with his twinkling blue eyes. "Why I make my camp far away in the frozen north. I have a log hut and a store of fuel and victuals. I put on my furs and I set off, setting my traps in a sort of circle, about a hundred miles round. Then I keep on walking around my traps. Sometimes I'm lucky, sometimes I'm not. I set the traps again according to the animal tracks I find. It takes a week, sometimes longer to do the round."

" What animals do you find? " Alison asked.

" It depends. All sorts, there's bear, of course, and wolves. And small fry like weasels, otters, marten and mink."

" Mink! " Alison exclaimed, " like film stars wear! "

" Aren't you ever lonely away up there? " said John.

" Trapping's a job for men who don't mind their own company, sonny. And I have my fiddle. "

" But Joe," said Alison, " why do you go to the far north in winter, when it's all frozen and horribly cold? "

" Why, missy, I go there because it *is* winter. The animals grow thick fur coats to keep warm, and that's the fur I want.

" You must know an awful lot about wild animals," said John, " and about camping, and finding your way about, and all the good things of life."

Old Joe laughed; " Well, I guess I'm learning! "

Alison asked Trapper Joe about the Eskimos in the far north of Canada. Joe lit his pipe carefully and blew out the match.

" The Canadian Eskimo, missy," he said, "is a mighty fine fellow, when you get to know him. I meet them when I go to the trading station at the end of the season."

" What are their igloos like? " asked John.

" Very snug," said Joe. "They only live in igloos in the winter, of course. In the summer Eskimos make tents of sealskin or such-like materials. They make the igloos out of blocks of hard-packed snow, and sometimes they line them with sealskin. Igloos look like old fashioned bee-hives. They burn a seal-oil lamp all the time, so they're proper cosy inside."

" I suppose they are hunters mainly? " said Alison.

" Hunters and fishers, and mighty clever, too," said Joe. "They hunt seals, from their kayaks, one-man canoes, in the summer, and at breathing-holes in the ice in winter. They eat the seal flesh, make clothes of the skin and use the oil for food and fuel. They hunt walruses, too, and the white fox, to trade the skins, and in the Fall they hunt the caribou. Oh, and whales in the summer."

" What about their dogs? " John asked.

" The huskies are the Eskimos' best friends. These dogs pull their sledges, and they couldn't manage without them. The Eskimos are good people; kind to their children and their old folk, and always cheerful. And you can always trust them. Yes, they're real fellows, are the Canadian Eskimos."

Trapper Joe also told them about the days when he went looking for gold. " It was a long time ago," he said, " when I was a lad. Great fortunes were being made by the lucky ones who found gold out in the Yukon."

" The Yukon Territory is in the far north-east of Canada, isn't it ? " asked John.

" That's right, north of British Columbia," said Joe. " They first found gold there in 1896, and that started what was called the Gold Rush. Men came from all over the world, men of every kind, but the only ones who could survive in the frozen wilderness of the Yukon were the tough ones. Some found gold, and I expect you know gold is one of Canada's most valuable industries. But most didn't, and I was one of them."

" My partner and I went to Dawson City—that's the capital of the Yukon—and spent all we had on our gear. We bought a sledge, furs, snow-boots, stores, a tent, axes and two good rifles."

" Rifles ? " said Alison.

" Yes, missy. There were tough men in the Yukon and it was lawless in those days. And there were the wolves."

" Wild wolves ? " said John, leaning forward.

" Wild wolves, laddie, and mighty hungry wolves, too. Many a time my partner and I sat by our camp fire at night in the deadly cold with the wolves waiting. Silent they were, and patient, and they looked at us and licked their lips. You could see their eyes glowing in the darkness. No, we didn't find gold, but it was a man's life and I reckon the experience I got was as valuable as gold."

Their father joined Alison and John after a business trip he had made alone, and the happy fortnight with their Canadian cousins came to an end. They finished as they had begun, with a party, and at the end they all sang old Canadian songs of the pioneering days, and 'Alouette,' the famous French-Canadian song, and 'Jingle Bells.' The next day they said good-bye and set off on the eight hundred mile journey westwards to Edmonton.

Edmonton is the capital of the province of Alberta. It is another busy, modern city which shows what a thriving country Canada is. Their father told them that Edmonton is the centre of the new Canadian oil industry, and the beginning of the famous Alaska Highway. This wonderful road goes for more than a thousand miles to the north-west, through the Yukon to Alaska.

They stayed in Edmonton for a few days and then went south to Calgary, another thriving and up-to-date city. They were very lucky, or their father had been very clever, for they got there in time to see the world-famous Calgary Stampede. Thousands of people had come to see this wild-west show, and all Calgary seemed to be in a holiday mood.

The enormous crowd loved the musical ride by thirty-two 'Mounties,' in their scarlet and blue uniforms, and applauded the clever horses. There was great excitement over the 'Chuck-wagon' races, when covered wagons like they used in the old days raced against each other. But Alison and John both voted that the best turn of all was the Bronco-busting. Cowboys in ten-gallon hats competed to see who could stay longest on a bucking, plunging, untamed horse.

"At last I've seen real cowboys in Canada," John said.

They had another treat in store. From Calgary they went to Banff, in the mountains eighty miles to the west, and their father had arranged it so that they were there during the annual Indian Days Festival.

" I *say*! " said John, his eyes shining, " in Calgary we saw real cowboys, and now we're going to see real Indians! "

" And just look at the scenery! " said Alison, gazing round. It was indeed wonderful. The town of Banff nestled in a rich valley nearly a mile up, with the mighty Rocky Mountains towering above, the snow-capped peaks shining in the sun.

At the Indian Festival they saw Chiefs in all the glory of feathered head-dresses. Braves rode bareback on galloping horses, shooting arrows with miraculous skill. They saw a war dance, and it was so realistic with the pulsing tom-toms that John said, not altogether jokingly, " I'm jolly glad they're friendly Indians! "

They saw all sorts of Indian work and bought some presents to take home; a blanket for their mother, a feathered head-dress for Peter, and an Indian doll for Mary. Their father bought Alison a lovely shawl and John a real Indian knife.

" Only about half the Indians in Canada live in the wilds," he said. " They live as they always have, by hunting, trapping and fishing. But the other half work with the whitemen, on farms, lumber camps and factories. Some Indians have become doctors, lawyers, teachers, clergymen and so on."

" Do the Indian children go to school? " John asked.

" Oh yes, the Canadian Government does all it can for its Indians. There are Reserves, areas reserved for them, and the Government sees to it that they have everything they need."

They spent several days at Banff. They hired a car and had some wonderful drives, including one to Lake Louise. The whole area is a National Park, so there is nothing to spoil the beauty of the mountain scenery. Their father told them that Banff is a famous place for winter sports, ski-ing, tobogganing and skating. " Canadians are good at all these," he said.

" And ice-hockey, too," said John.

" It's the national winter sport in Canada," said their father.

" Golly," said Alison, " fancy being so good at skating that you can play hockey on skates? "

They left Banff to drive all the way to Vancouver. That three-day drive through the Rocky Mountains was something they will never forget. Their father told them that the Rocky Mountains stretch from the north of Canada, right down the United States, and then on down Mexico.

Once when they had stopped for a picnic lunch they were delighted to see three bears lumber out of the woods towards them. The children knew then why they had brought a large bag of buns. The bears seemed to know too! When they had made friends, John got out his note-book and wrote BEARS at the top of a page. Then he looked enquiringly at his father.

" These are black bears," he said, and John wrote it down. " They live all over Canada and are often quite friendly. Then there are the grizzly bears, but they are *not* tame. They're very large. The other kind are the white Polar bears, in the far north, and they're not tame either."

" But these are," said Alison, " look at them! Aren't they sweet! "

As they drove through the Rocky Mountains they passed from Alberta into British Columbia, the most western province of Canada. British Columbia is on the Pacific coast and it is perhaps the most beautiful part of the country. It has many islands, such as Vancouver and the Queen Charlotte group of islands.

" There must be simply miles and miles of forests in Canada," Alison said, as they drove down a road lined with thick forest.

" Nearly a third of Canada is forest land," her father said, " and she is one of the biggest exporters of timber in the world, especially wood to make into paper."

" I expect that's why we saw so many ships loaded with enormous tree-trunks in Montreal and Quebec," said John. " I made a note of it in my book," he added.

Soon afterwards their father stopped the car and they got out to see all the interesting things which he pointed out. A wide river was flowing on one side of the road, and it was full of tree-trunks. Men were stepping about on them with amazing agility. They steered the tree-trunks and kept them straight by using long poles. Alison and John watched, quite fascinated.

" That's how they take the trees down to the saw-mills," their father said. " The Canadian lumber-jacks, as they are called, are extraordinary chaps. They live in camps in the forest, miles from anywhere, make tracks through the forest, fell the trees and drag them down these tracks to the river. They steer them over rapids, make dams where the river is too shallow, and—well—look at them now! "

Alison, John and their father stood on the beach of a little town on the west coast of Vancouver Island and looked out to sea.

" Now we have really come right across Canada," said Alison.

" Yes, it's more than four thousand miles from St. John's in Newfoundland, and that's the most easterly point in Canada. Now we are on the most westerly."

" And this is the Pacific Ocean! " said John.

" Then let's get into it," said Alison. " Let's have our swim."

" I'll race you! " John shouted.

Soon they were splashing and swimming in the Pacific Ocean.

After the swim they dressed and had lunch, and then their father took them to see some totem poles. They gazed up at the high and elaborately carved poles in amazement.

" What are they? " John asked.

" Pine trees, carved by the Indians as guardian spirits. They are found all over the Pacific coast of Canada."

" Look at this," said Alison, " it's got a bird on top."

" That's a raven," said her father. " And look, there's a bear, with a mother bear and a cub. They have all sorts of animals and birds, and people, too. They aren't found anywhere else in the world, so have a good look. "

Alison got out her sketch book and John took some snap-shots. Then he started writing in his notebook.

He said, " How do they carve these figures so high up?"

" Ah, that's a question you must ask an Indian."

Their visit to Vancouver Island was made from Vancouver, where they were staying for ten days. When their father was busy, the wife of one of his friends took Alison and John for trips to the parks and beauty spots, and they saw the miles of orchard lands. They found Vancouver itself an exciting city, with the new and busy look of all Canadian cities they had seen.

One day their father took them to the port, and told them something about it.

" Vancouver is a very young city," he explained. " It was only born in 1885, when the Canadian Pacific Railway was finished. By getting the railway through to the west coast all Canada was opened up. So Vancouver was born as a city—and look at it now! "

" It's a tremendous port," said John, looking round him.

" Vancouver has the finest natural harbour in the world. All the wheat grown in Alberta is shipped from Vancouver, as well as the timber, fruit, fish and other products of British Columbia," their father explained.

They wandered round the port and saw ships from countries all over the world. They saw the gigantic grain elevators pouring the golden wheat into the ships' holds. Timber was being loaded into other ships, and also hundreds of very large rolls which their father explained was paper, made from logs which had been floated down rivers. They were being sent to other countries to be made into newspapers. There was cargo of all kinds, the riches of Canada, going out to customers all over the world.

At last the time came to begin the long journey home. For a final treat their father had arranged for them to travel on *The Canadian*, a luxury, stream-lined, stainless steel train. *The Canadian* crosses Canada from Vancouver to Montreal, a distance of 2,881 miles, in seventy hours. Alison and John were very excited to be travelling in this famous train, and at spending two days and three nights in it. Their father had booked seats in a Dome Observation coach, so that they would have a clear view of the countryside.

The train left Vancouver at 8 o'clock on Friday evening, and they were due in Montreal at 9 o'clock on Monday morning. When the train had pulled out they explored their part of it, had supper and went to bed in their comfortable little cabins.

They were up early the next morning and watched the wonderful scenery as the train climbed through the Rocky Mountains. After lunch they got to Lake Louise, five thousand feet up. All day they watched the mountain scenery unfold, and they stayed up until nine o'clock so that they could see the station at Medicine Hat. John wanted to be woken at two in the morning so that he could see Moose Jaw, but his father refused.

They made friends on the train, enjoyed the wonderful meals, and were far too busy to make sketches or write facts in a notebook. The long journey went on, through the prairie lands, through Winnipeg, Port Arthur and so to Ottawa and finally Montreal. The train pulled in exactly on time.

" Now that's what I call a train journey," said John.

Before they went up the gangway into the air-liner at Montreal, Alison and John turned and had a last look at Canada. Inside they took their seats and fastened their safety belts. The stewardess brought round sweets and they took one each to suck while the air-liner was climbing. Soon the engines roared, they began to move, accelerated until they were racing down the runway and then—they were airborne. The plane circled Montreal once, as though to say good-bye, and set course for Gander in the north of Newfoundland, and then across the Atlantic Ocean for Britain.

When they had unfastened their safety belts and settled down, their father said, " Well, you've seen some-of Canada. Now, what do you remember best? "

" The Mounties," said John quickly, " and the cowboys at Calgary and the Indians at Banff."

" I remember those darling bears," Alison said, " and dreamy old Quebec and the nice French-Canadians."

" Niagara Falls," John declared, " and that voyage across the lakes, and Trapper Joe and his tales of the Northland."

" I remember the holiday with Uncle James, and how kind they were to us," Alison said.

" That's good, but what about Canada itself ? "

" Well, it's very big, and very rich, and everyone seems to work very hard, and they're happy," said Alison thoughtfully.

John pondered the question, and then he said, " I think Canada is like someone who is growing up. Some-one strong and clever."

" That's it," said their father. " Canada is very rich. And everyone works jolly hard not only to make Canada rich, but great."

CANADA

Edmonton

VANCOUVER

Banff • Calgary

VANCOUVER ISLAND

Winnipeg

Port Arthur

MONTREAL

Quebec

Toronto

Halifa

NOVA SCO

OTTAWA

U.S.A.

PACIFIC OCEAN

AIR ROUTE TRAVELLED BY
ALISON AND JOHN AND
THE TOWNS THEY VISITED

SOUTH AMERIC